You Always Matter

Author: Sarita Dillard - Illustrator: Melarie Odelusi

YOU ALWAYS MATTER
Author: Sarita Dillard
Illustrator: Melarie Odelusi

Copyright © 2020
Sarita Dillard Picture Book Ages 4-7 Houston,
P.O. Box 924732, Houston , TX 77292
youalwaysmatterbook@gmail.com

ISBN: 978-0-578-87414-2

This is a work of fiction. All of the characters, names, incidents, organizations, and dialogue in this work are either the products of the author's imagination or are used fictitiously.

Bird House Publishing Services rev date: 12.09.2019
First Edition

Author's Dedication:

To my children, may you always know your self-worth.
May you always remember to let your light shine.
Everything I do is for you. My prayer is that this book is a
constant reminder to you, and future generations, of how
far we have come. The world is yours, and mommy will
always be your biggest supporter. I love you.

Illustrator's Dedication:

To the coolest kids I know, you are loved, chosen and
powerful because God says you are. Never forget that.
I love you Kai and Emmie. - Mommy

A history full of kings and queens from a land where lions and giraffes roam free.

From grasslands to pyramids to everything in between, you are from a legendary dynasty.

YOU MATTER.

From head to toe,
covered in glistening gold.
Curly coiled hair.
Bold cheekbones. Full lips.

EVERY IMPERFECTION MATTERS.

Know that your melanin runs far and wide.
We are a people of vast numbers.
ENDLESS differences. Shades and colors.

From Southern Asia to Northern Africa. From the Pacific to the Atlantic Ocean. **WE ALL MATTER.**

Our ancestors marched
to ensure equality for generations
to come. **JUSTICE. PEACE.**
LIBERATION for all.

Even the smallest steps and the tiniest of feet can continue the **FIGHT** for **JUSTICE** for you and for me.

Others before you have walked
similar paths of adversity.
Someone's brother. Someone's sister.
Someone's son. Someone's daughter.
No loss to be forgotten.

May we always say the names of
those who stared injustice in the eye.
Let them continue to inspire our fight.

THEY ALL MATTER.

From astronauts to educators.
From engineers to physicians.
From attorneys to athletes to the
vice president and president of
the United States of America.

There is not a dream
too big nor a star too high.

CHANGE THE WORLD.

Be the change.
The **FUTURE** is yours.

There will come
a time and place
where people will be
unfair or unkind.

Fear can often make others act
or say very hurtful things.

They may be challenged by your uniqueness. Intimidated by your courage.

THREATENED BY YOUR RESILIENCE.

It is not always easy to understand
the mean things people may say or do.

STAND TALL. Know your history.
Always speak up for kindness and equality.

Remember there is no color to love.

We are all **CREATED EQUAL.**

Let every day be a reminder of your worth. With every breath, know that you matter. You were hand chosen to walk a path of **GREATNESS.** Adversity is nothing more than a stepping stone toward your **SUCCESS.**

Hold your head high and
make sure your crown sits tall.
Always walk with kindness in your
heart and purity in your soul.

CARRY THE TORCH,

young kings and queens.

CPSIA information can be obtained
at www.ICGtesting.com
Printed in the USA
BVRC100213310821
615632BV00001B/2